3D Printer

A Complete 3D Printing Guide

Milton Don Randall

D1453279

reparation, damages, or monetary loss incurred as a result of the information contained herein, either explicitly or implicitly.

All copyrights not held by the publisher are owned by the respective author(s).

The information contained herein is provided solely for informational purposes and is therefore universal. The information is presented without contract or assurance of any kind.

The trademarks are used without the trademark owner's consent, and the trademark is published without the trademark owner's permission or support. All trademarks and brands mentioned in this book are solely for clarity purposes and are owned by their respective owners, who are not affiliated with this document.

ISBN: 978-1-63750-279-2

Table of Contents

Free Bonus

Grab My *"Social Media Marketing Made Simple"* Ebook For **FREE!**

Today you can grab your copy of my Free e-book titled –
Social Media Marketing made Simple. Best of all, it won't cost you a thing.

Click the image above to **Download the Book,** and also Subscribe for Free books, giveaways, and new releases by me.

https://mayobook.com/milton

Introduction

3D printing is changing the world. Whether you know it or not, it has already changed yours. The technology behind the new 3D printing revolution is so much more than a fancy toy. It has real-world applications that go beyond making plastic replicas of your favorite movie characters and even offer the promise of bioprinting human organs.

3D printing is a fast-growing technology that is changing our world by making it possible to quickly build physical objects from a digital design. It's also creating a thriving community of designers, engineers, artists, and hobbyists who are learning how to 3D print all kinds of objects, such as jewelry, gadgets, art pieces, and more.

Whether you want to start with a basic intro to the technology or dive deep into 3D printing topics like the 3D printer file formats, 3D printing tools, or 3D printing software, this book has got you covered.

I am going to explain the basics of how 3D printing works. We'll start with the basics of what a 3D printer is and how it works before we dig into the technical details. Once you understand the basics, you'll be able to make sense of the buzz around the technology and decide whether or not this is something that would benefit you.

3D printing is taking the world by storm! Whether you're curious to learn more about this cutting-edge technology or if you've been following 3D printing news for a while, here's the lowdown on what you need to know about 3D printing. 3D printing is changing the way we create things. Whether you want to use your 3D printer to design your next project, print something for yourself, or sell it to someone else, here are three key areas you need to focus on to make the most of this technology.

This book will give you a step-by-step guide to get started with 3D printing, including where to buy the supplies and software, what types of things you can make, and some common mistakes to avoid.

3D printers can be used for a number of things. They're usually used to make items for themselves or others—including *food, jewelry, artwork, toys, and even prosthetics.* These objects are typically produced by melting and/or hardening various materials. Depending on the specific printer, there are many different types of materials available that can be used for the printer to create whatever object is desired.

The most basic printers use plastics like polycarbonate, ABS plastic, and nylon, which are heated up and hardened. The printer then creates a 3D object by using layers of the material.

The most popular type of 3D printer is probably the fused deposition modeling (FDM) printer. This printer uses a heated nozzle to melt and deposit layers of plastic into a box or frame that is being built. The printer uses one or more extruders that push the melted plastic through the nozzle. Once the extruder reaches its target temperature, it deposits the layer of plastic. The layers of plastic are then stacked on top of each other until the entire object is completed.

3D printers are making their way into businesses and homes, making them readily available to anyone with a little cash and patience. As these printers become more affordable, people are finding a use for them in the home. From jewelry to pens, a 3D printer can be used to create a wide variety of products. These products are typically made from plastics and metals and require no other tools. The cost of 3D printing has come down significantly over the last couple of years. Most manufacturers of 3D printers are able to produce a basic model that costs under $1000. The price has dropped as the technology has become more accessible. However, the quality of these printers is still quite high. The latest models offer high-resolution prints at very fast speeds. The quality of these prints will improve over time, but the initial quality is already high. This technology is also being used in the medical industry.

What is 3D printing?

3D printing is a technology that creates objects by creating layers of material and building up the object. The most common types of 3D printing are called additive manufacturing and subtractive manufacturing. In additive manufacturing, layers of material are added to the object one layer at a time. In subtractive manufacturing, an object is created from a block of material that is cut away. The most popular materials for 3D printing are plastic, metal, and ceramic.

How does 3D printing work?

The basic steps of 3D printing include: Material selection.

The first step is to select the right material for the job. This can be anything from plastic to metal to ceramic. Some materials are better for making small objects. Others are better for large or complicated objects. Materials selection is often done in combination with design software to ensure that the finished product will look the way the designer wants it to.

Printing the design: The next step is to print out a representation of the object, usually in the form of a 3D model. Once the model is printed, the next step is to add material to it. This can be done in one of two ways: Additive manufacturing. In additive manufacturing, layers of material are added one at a time, building up the object. This type of printing uses a computer-aided design (CAD) software package that can create the models used in printing. For example, a CAD program could be used to create a model of an ear for 3D printing, using a plastic material. The software then creates a three-dimensional file, which can be used to print an ear. Subtractive manufacturing.

In subtractive manufacturing, a solid block of material is removed from a larger block to make the final shape. This type of printing is usually done with a laser or an electron beam, and is typically more expensive than additive manufacturing. Once the print is finished, the part is usually sanded down to smooth it out.

The final step is to coat the surface of the part with a protective coating. This can be done with a powder coating. This powder is then melted into the surface of the part using a heated tool called a sinter gun. The final step is to apply any finishing touches. This can include adding a gloss finish to the part, painting, or simply polishing.

Chapter 1

3D Printing

To 3D print a physical object, you'll need a computer model in three dimensions. Almost any shape can be achieved with minimal effort by layering materials, typically in the form of a coating.

A modern technology like *3D printing* has the potential to fundamentally alter the way we interact with the world. Although it is already being utilized by amateurs, medical experts, and even some businesses, this intriguing new technology has a long way to go before it is widely adopted.

It's possible, though, that you can profit from this new technology if you're willing to put in the time and effort required. A look at the many sorts of 3D printers available, how they function, and why they're (or aren't) ideal for various purposes will be covered in this book.

What precisely is 3D printing, and how does it differ from other printing methods?

3-dimensional product creation by *"printing"* material

layers one after the other, one at a time. This process is known as **<u>additive manufacturing (AM).</u>** *Additive and Subtractive 3D printers are currently the most common.*

To build an object, an additive printer applies many layers of plastic or another substance. To make an object, a subtractive printer begins with a block of material and gradually removes pieces of it. Both laser and inkjet printers have advantages and downsides. Let's compare and contrast them.

Additive-based 3D printing: Additive 3D printing is comparable to the process of building a house, where a computer model is utilized to manufacture an object step-by-step. Layers of thermoplastic or other materials are used to create the final product. Welding occurs when a powerful heat source passes over the layers and causes them to melt and then solidify back into their original state.

To begin with, there was the *"Fused Deposition Modeling,"* or **"FDM,"** additive printer. This printer is similar to a fax machine in that it utilizes very expensive paper to communicate. To make the thing, the printer extrudes tiny thermoplastic or other material beads one at a time and fuses them together on the build platform, which is a continuous roll of that paper. Fused deposition is the name given to this technique because the plastic layers are fused together as the process proceeds. A variety of **FDM** printers are available on the market: "heated-bed" printers are the most common.

They're also the priciest ones. An additive printer that uses a *heated bed* operates like this: Material is unwound from a spool and fed into a melting chamber in a continuous stream. *An aperture (the print head)* is then used to melt the filament into a liquid condition. Upon exiting the print head, the filament is driven onto the build platform, which is a horizontal, pre-heated, steel surface.

There are normally three axes on this platform, which allows the printer to deposit filament in any direction. *Layers* are built up as the platform goes forward, adding more hardened filament. Multiple *orifices* on a print head allow *filament* to be extruded at the same time. The diameter of these orifices is just a few thousandths of an inch. The size of the ejected bead is determined by the diameter of each aperture.

An *FDM printer* is capable of producing beads as small as 0.05 inches in size. Infrared (IR) radiation or a high-powered laser is used to fuse the beads together into a single piece. To create the object, successive layers of plastic are melted together and then fused together as the building platform goes forward. <u>Until the complete model is printed, this process is repeated.</u>

Note that all layers of plastic must be fused together in order to create a model that is sturdy and effective.

It is possible that the model will fail if any of the layers are not properly fused. The material used in an additive printer is called ***"filament."***

Filament is made up of individual tiny plastic or other beads, which are glued together. The size of these beads is extremely important. The smaller they are, the more detail you will be able to create in your model. On the other hand, if the beads are too small, they will fuse together when the printer heats them up, and you will get a very weak model.

Subtractive-based 3D printing:
Subtractive manufacturing is an umbrella term for various controlled machining and material removal processes that start with solid blocks, bars, rods of plastic, metal, or other

materials that are shaped by removing material through cutting, boring, drilling, and grinding.

Computer numerical control (CNC) is used to do these tasks, but they can also be done manually (CNC). **CAD software** is used to create a virtual model that may be used as an input for the fabrication tool on a CNC machine. Using software simulation and user input, toolpaths are generated that guide the cutting tool through the part's geometric shape. In these instructions, the machine is told how to make the appropriate cuts and channels, holes, and any other characteristics that require material removal, taking into account the cutting tool's speed and material feed rate. This computer-aided manufacturing (CAM) data is used by CNC equipment to produce parts without the need for human intervention or help.

3D Printers' Working Principles

Most people utilize Fused Deposition Modeling **(FDM)** at home to print 3D objects **(FDM)**. It is powered by a filament, similar to a string, that is made of plastic. When a heated filament is run through the plastic material, it melts. Parts are molded from molten plastic extruded from the machine's top. In order to begin depositing the second layer, the top of the first is lifted by the amount of thickness that was deposited on it. Layer by layer, the components are put together.

Finishing can be done in any way chosen once all layers have been applied to the piece. This procedure is repeated until the portion is finished. Unlike **FDM, Selective Laser Sintering (SLS)** employs a plastic filament. Instead of using a regular hot mind, a laser is employed to melt the plastic. Because of this, the method is also known as *"binder" or "selective" laser sintering*, in which the melted plastic is incorporated into the material that was previously sintering. The part is built layer by layer until it is completed. **Stereolithography (SLA)** is a little more unique.

It operates similarly to a light machine. On a flat surface, a liquid plastic material is spread out. The object is then exposed to a special ultraviolet light. The light hardens and cures the plastic. At the thickness of one layer, the platform is lowered, and more of the liquid plastic is dispensed onto it. After that, the stage is raised, and the procedure is repeated once more. It is possible to create extremely thin and complex objects using stereolithography technology. Dental professionals can use it to make a model of the patient's mouth so they can determine what needs to be done to correct the patient's teeth. Using **SLA** in a variety of ways is practically limitless. Moreover, it is the most expensive of all the 3D printing methods. A flat surface is also required for this method, as it is the only one. If the platform on which the object is being created has any bumps or unevenness, none of the other 3D printing methods will work.

Using a 3D Printer Effectively

In either case, print off a **3D model** you've downloaded, or make your own. **Grab CAD** or **Thingiverse** are good places to look for free *CAD models*. A model can be built using Google Sketch Up or Blender. **CAD software** like **SolidWorks** is utilized to create executive parts. For *3D printing purposes*, save your model as an **STL** or **OBJ** file.

3D slicing software like **Cura** or **MakerWare** can be used to cut out the desired shapes from your model. It's a no-brainer to use **MakerWare** with a MakerBot 3D printer. A wide range of 3D printers can use the **G-code** produced by **Cura** and **Simplify 3D.**

In order to properly set up your slicing program, you must first decide how to place your model on the 3D Inkjet printer. The use of **FDM** should be avoided if the overhangs are steeper than 45 degrees because they require the development of support structures.

Layers should not be accelerated by over-packing your model; this is analogous to exploiting the grain in wood. In addition, the model's support structures can be moved about.

The *"view"* *option* in the slicer can be used to make modifications. The slicer's ***"view"*** option can be used to adjust the model's orientation. For best results, the build plate must be at least as thick as the layer height.

Print your model in **PLA** or **ABS** if possible. Watch the extrusion width closely. Within the appropriate range, it should be.

In order to ensure proper heat dispersion, always print on a level surface. Surfaces that are smooth and solid are ideal. Make adjustments to the temperature of the bed as needed after each layer. Make sure that you are printing in the correct orientation if you see any warping.

The heated bed of your 3D printer should be set to the correct temperature. Extruder gear must be thoroughly cleaned.

Before beginning a print, check to see that your filament is centered. Only print one side of the model at a time to avoid warping. The model should be printed as a whole, with the support structure at the bottom if you have one. Avoid using support structures for large or complex models. When printing on a heated bed, use a fan that is blowing the other way.

Structural Supports for 3-D Printing

Because it saves time and resources, models aren't reliable. An infill percentage of between 10% and 35%, including 1-2 perimeter levels as well as bottom and top levels, is normal (typically 2-4). Other considerations should be made when prepping your model for 3D printing.

G-code files are typically used to export this software. *Slicing software* will help you turn your model and the instructions you've received into a set of instructions for building. This data will be used by your 3D printer to build the part. To install this program on your 3D inkjet printer, connect your computer through **USB, SD card, or Wi-Fi.**

In order to remove and clean the 3D printer after printing your object, you will need to follow these steps:

Use the best sandpaper to eliminate any leftover lumps from the supporting structures. Because of this, you should realize that 3D printing doesn't necessitate structural support. They do, however, have the advantage of being able to print on a very flat surface.

If you decide to use structural supports, here are some things to keep in mind: *Assistive material Laser printers and inkjet printers* don't always print the same. For the most part, a laser printer can only print in black and white.

Inkjet printers are capable of printing many colors at the same time. Laser printers, on the other hand, tend to have rougher surfaces. Because of this, you'll need supporting material.

If you want to acquire the finest outcomes, you also need to take into account the type of support material you employ. Laser printers can handle some materials, while inkjet printers can handle others. Here are a few typical sources of assistance, to name a few:

Drilling small holes into the surface of the model can also be done with a drill bit. Different materials are used to make 3D printing supports. Among the most prevalent are those made from plastic, metal, and wood. Plastic **SupportsPlastic** is the most frequently utilized support material. Plastic is widely used. You'll need a filament extruder in this situation. An **ABS filament** is required if you want to print your object in *ABS (acrylonitrile butadiene styrene)*. This is a common material that can be found at most stores. For use in your 3D printer, you must ensure that it is compatible with your machine. If you want to print in ***HIPS (high impact polystrene)***, you'll need *polyethylene terephthalate glycol filament*. This is a common material that can be found at most stores. For use in your 3D printer, you must ensure that it is compatible with your machine.

Different Types of 3D printers that Exist

Rapid prototyping was the earliest use of 3D printing, and hence, it was referred to as **"3D printing."** When discussing *3D printing*, the term "additive manufacturing" is usually used to describe the process. The term **"3D printing"** refers to both professional additive manufacturing and home 3D printing.

For *industrial additive manufacturing*, **3D laser printers** are the most common tool. Powdered or liquid chemicals can be stored in tanks on them. A laser beam is used to etch the material's top surface with a varying profile. Using ***UV lasers***, resin is converted into a solid plastic. They can be used to fuse powdered plastic, metal, or ceramic together using high-powered lasers.

An early **3D printer** that was available to consumers was the **Desktop Metal Solidoodle (DMS)**. Additive manufacturing is used to create this machine, although no platform is necessary. There is a lot of aluminum and steel in the **Solidoodle's** main body.

The first desktop 3D printer has been around for more than a decade, but the technology has improved dramatically. It's only a matter of time until 3D printing takes off in the household. Because desktop 3D printers have become more affordable, this is the case. A wide variety of 3D printers are available nowadays. Some are pricey, while others are modest in price, and still others are within your reach.

An advanced laser sintering 3D printer, such as the **MakerBot Replicator**, can cost thousands of dollars to buy and operate. In terms of accuracy, it's the best method for printing parts. Most popular consumer-grade 3D printers, including **Formlabs' Form 1**, are also pricey. From $500 to $2,000, these machines are available. Desktop 3D printers are also available at a modest cost.

The Future of 3D Printing is bright

With a 3D printer in your house, you'll be able to make anything. Your clothes, vehicle parts, and even your dinner will all be available for you to download and print in the future. These claims should be viewed with a grain of salt. Using 3D printers, ten homes a day may be built in China for under $5,000 apiece, according to an incredible statement. Each 3D-printed house had just one room devoted to printing the wall space, which accounted for less than 10% of the overall cost of the building.

Other than that, most of the construction costs aren't allocated to the construction of the foundation for the building. Household plumbing, electrical work, and woodworking can easily add up in price. So, don't expect to get a new house for $5,000.

3D printing's future is closer than you would imagine. There is a lot more to 3D printing than you might believe. For the first time, it's no longer a specialist technology used only by amateurs or experts. There are a lot of areas where 3D printing has the potential to be disruptive, including aerospace, medical technology, military hardware, and even automobiles.

3D printing will be used in a wide range of new ways in

the coming decade. 3D printing has a wide range of uses. A new generation of 3D printers can now produce objects that are virtually identical to their traditional counterparts.

You must answer the question, _"What do I want to print?"_ if you're interested in 3D printing.

Products made from 3D printing are widely used in the fields of _architecture, transportation, and medicine._ Currently, a lot of 3D-printed things are being designed and manufactured. **3D printing** is a cutting-edge technology that is constantly evolving. While 3D printing has been around since the 1980s, firms began employing it to produce consumer goods in the early 2000s. 3D printing will be used in a wide range of new ways in the coming decade. 3D printing has a wide range of uses.

What Purposes do 3D Printers Serve?

It has been common practice for many years to use 3D printing to swiftly produce low-strength prototypes. Now that 3D printing is more affordable, it's a great option for home modelers. Kitchen appliances and furniture knobs and handles can also be replaced with these parts. It is possible to use *3D printing* for components that don't require a lot of strength.

Engineers in the aerospace industry have long relied on 3D printers to create lightweight and sturdy components. It's possible that 3D printing is more cost-effective than traditional manufacturing methods at certain times. Additionally, 3D-printed cell scaffolds for specific regions of the body are increasingly being used in medical research.

For 3D printing, some businesses are even developing their own 3D printing machines. It is possible to use a 3D printer to make a wide variety of household items at home. Businesses can benefit from 3D printing as well. Occasionally, 3D printing is used to build prototypes for items that will be manufactured using traditional methods.

What Can 3D Printers be used to Create?

Models of real-world objects can be made using 3D printers. <u>A 3D printer is capable of creating a model from scratch based on a design</u>. There are a variety of 3D printers to choose from. It is possible to create a final product with desktop printers that use inkjet printing and laser cutting.

Industrial printers, on the other hand, are more common. *Extrusion, injection molding, or other methods are used to make their parts.* Many different things can be made with a 3D printer. Some printers are used to make prototypes of products. Others are used to make spare parts or production models. Printing practical goods like jewelry, shoes, or other small items is a common use for some printers.

A Primer on 3D Printers

3D printing might be a challenge to learn. There are a lot of newbies who may not know where to start, which is why you bought this book. There are a few things to consider before diving headfirst into the realm of 3D printing.

In this section, we'll address the most frequently asked questions by those who are just getting started with 3D printing.

A 3D printer is recommended but not essential. A desktop 3D printer is now within the reach of everyone. The first and most important consideration should be to get a **3D**

inkjet printer. Online resources for language learning can provide you with printable models that you can order and receive by mail.

If you need to print anything from time to time, sending a blueprint to one of these companies may be your best option.

A 3D printer that can be used on a daily basis should be taken into account when making a purchase. The practice of 3D printing is now more than simply a passing fancy. In recent years, it has become a growing industry. The global 3D printer market is predicted to be worth $7 billion in 2015. This industry is predicted to grow by a factor of two between now and 2023. If you intend to use a 3D printer on a regular basis, you should get started as soon as possible.

Are 3D printers and CNC machines different?

Before we get started, let's have a look at 3D printing. Making real products from three-dimensional (3D) models is now possible thanks to the invention of 3D printing. A wide range of materials can be used, including plastic, metal, and even wood. It is possible to use the phrase *"3D printing"* to refer not only to the process of creating an object, but also to the finished product. **"CNC"** is an acronym for **"Computer Numerical Control.**

What Printer Should You Purchase if You Decide to do so?

The truth is, you'll need a **3D printer** for your project. You're about to make a life-altering purchase. Pre-assembled machines or scratch-built machines are the only options. <u>Both routes have advantages and disadvantages.</u> If you're self-sufficient and well-versed in your profession, the second option may be more appealing to you. Building a 3D inkjet printer yourself will cost money, but it is not for the faint of heart.

<u>If something goes wrong with your 3D printer in the future, you'll be prepared to remove and reassemble it because you already know how.</u>

It's possible to find a pre-assembled 3D printer for about $500, but customizing one can easily cost upwards of $2,500. *Extrusion and fused deposition modeling* are the two most frequent printing methods **(FDM).** Using a heated filament, extrusion printers extrude plastic.

Hot melt is deposited layer-by-layer in an **FDM** printer's heated chamber. When building a 3D printer, there are a few things to keep in mind. In theory, anyone may construct their own 3D printer, but this book is aimed at novices or beginners. Pre-assembled 3D printers are the only option if you don't have the resources or expertise to make your own.

It's great that 3D printers are getting cheaper while still advancing in terms of decision-making and quality.

There are plans for 3D models to be found. When it comes to accessing the product design blueprints, options include both online and in-house approaches. Models are available on the **ThingVerse** website. This site is owned by **MakerBot**, but there is still a good selection of plans from *non-MakingBot users*.

Where Will You Get Your Materials From?

Engineers formerly invented **CAD software**, which is now widely used by other engineers. Although it is still organic in nature, **CAD software** is now more approachable and can be used efficiently by anyone with the proper training. Because of the steep learning curve of

CAD software, today's **CAD software** is geared toward non-technical consumers. **Modern CAD software** is easier to learn and use than it used to be, but the learning curve remains high, and you'll need to devote a significant amount of time and effort to mastering the concepts of *3D printer-ready design using* **CAD software**.

Check out **Autodesk's 123D Design** and **Inventor Fusion** to learn the basics of **CAD design software**. Both of these applications can be downloaded for free with a limited license. If you want to print models, you should use the free versions of the software tools available.

It's important to keep in mind, though, that the free/limited/student versions of **CAD software** don't often allow you to market your printed things or even sell the data you make. It's usually a good idea to check out the license information before downloading any software.

A commercial software license is required if you plan to use 3D printing for business purposes. Inquiring minds want to know if it is feasible to download and print files. If you're looking for a 3D scanning company, you're in luck! Consider 3D. The scanned models, on the other hand, typically require a lot of work before they can be utilized for printing.

For the time being, it's better to produce the documents "yourself" and then print them off rather than wait for a service that can accomplish this for you.

How Do You Print Models You've Downloaded?

In most cases, models obtained from **Thingverse** will already be in **STL** format. By following the **STL** file's instructions attentively, you can change that **STL** file into something quite extraordinary.

Sliced look files are necessary for an inkjet printer to work with them; this means that the object's temperature, velocity, and wall thickness settings must be mapped out layer-by-layer. **Inkjet printers** can read the **G-Code** document produced by this technique.

Several free slicing programs exist, including **ReplicatorG** and **Curand KISSlicer**.

G-Code can be generated from STL files using **ReplicatorG**, a free open-source application. Direct printing from a computer is also an option with inkjet printers. It will, however, take longer to print than if you used an **SD card**. When it comes to printing, the possibilities are nearly limitless. It all depends on the printer you have. Some inkjet printers can create anything from a laser to an origami robot, while others can only print 3D objects. **3D printing** is widely used to create prototypes, one of the most common applications. 3D printing is a great option if you want to produce a real embodiment of your concept.

What's the best way to print the models you've made?

Slicing software can be a crucial part of the process of creating your final, printable file. A computer-aided design program can export your model as an STL file if you used that software to create your model. All you need to do is utilize slicing software to transform it into a **G-Code** document.

A 3D application like **Photoshop** or **Sketchup**, as well as any other *3D design program* that isn't specifically designed for **CAD**, necessitates many procedures to obtain the **G code** document.

Check to determine if the model is truly printable before printing it out in any other way. Patching up holes and correcting vertices are usually all that is required.

In order to slice it for the printer, the file must first be converted to an **STL**. Both the patching of the model and the creation of the **STL** file should be performed using **Meshlab**, a free and open-source tool. There is a commercial tool called **NetFabb** that can generate **G-Code** data files as well.

Summary

3D printing has the potential to fundamentally alter the way we interact with the world. *Additive and subtractive 3D printers* are currently the most common. Both laser and inkjet printers have advantages and disadvantages; here's a look at how they compare and work. An FDM printer is capable of producing beads as small as 0.05 inches in size. **Infrared (IR) radiation** or a high-powered laser is used to fuse the beads together into a single piece.

Subtractive manufacturing is an umbrella term for various controlled machining and material removal processes.

Computer numerical control (CNC) machines can produce parts without the need for human intervention. **CAD software** is used to create a virtual model that may be used as an input for the fabrication tool on a CNC machine. The **computer-aided manufacturing (CAM)** data is used by CNC equipment to produce parts. **SLA** is the most expensive of all the 3D printing methods.

It operates similarly to a light machine. A flat surface is required for this method, as it is the only one that creates an exact replica of the object you're trying to create using 3D software. Prepping your model for 3-D printing is important. Always print on a level surface to ensure proper heat dispersion. Avoid using support structures for large or complex models.

Use the best sandpaper to remove any leftover lumps from the supporting structures after each print. Different materials are used to make 3D printing supports. Among the most prevalent are those made from plastic, metal, and wood. For use in your 3D printer, you must ensure that it is compatible with your machine. 3D laser printers are the most common tool for industrial additive manufacturing.

Desktop 3D printers have become more affordable. Ten homes a day may be built in China for under $5,000 apiece. 3D printing will be used in a wide range of new ways in the coming decade. It's no longer a specialist technology used only by amateurs or experts. 3D printing is a cutting-edge technology that is constantly evolving.

Products made from 3D printing are widely used in the fields of architecture, transportation, and medicine. It is possible to use a 3D printer to make a wide variety of household items at home. The global 3D printer market is predicted to be worth $7 billion in 2015. Pre-assembled machines or scratch-built machines are the only options. Building a 3D inkjet printer yourself will cost money, but it is not for the faint of heart.

Pre-assembled 3D printers are the only option if you don't have the resources or expertise to make your own. **Modern CAD software** is easier to learn and use than it used to be, but the learning curve remains high. It can cost upwards of $2,500 to custom-make a **3D printer**. Sliced look files are necessary for an inkjet printer to work with them. Free slicing programs exist, including **ReplicatorG** and **Curand KISSlicer**.

Direct printing from a computer is also an option with inkjet printers. It will, however, take longer to print than if you used an SD card. 3D printing is widely used to create prototypes, one of the most common applications. Slicing software can be a crucial part of the process of creating your final, printable file. Some inkjet printers can create anything from a laser to an **origami robot**.

Chapter 2

Choosing a 3D Printer and its Uses

3D printing is experiencing a resurgence akin to that of computing in the early 1970s. Sectors that could afford to purchase expensive 3D printers were the first to make use of this new technology. To make the new technology more accessible to hobbyists and those interested in experimenting, desktop 3D printers have been developed.

This technology has a wide range of applications and is frequently used in education, as we have shown in previous chapter.

The way manufacturing is done has undergone a tremendous transformation.

Commercial manufacturing uses assembly lines to assemble multiple parts before the final product takes shape. The arrival of 3D printing will fundamentally disrupt current production practices.

An inkjet printer at a manufacturing facility may print entire products by sending a computer-generated design to the printer. Assembly lines are no longer necessary.

When compared to subtractive manufacturing, 3D printing is constrained by its additive production restrictions. The preceding method, on the other hand, employs no specific tools as it constructs the item layer by layer. Using 3D printers, even the most complex designs can be produced with ease, so designers no longer have to be concerned about how they will be printed.

In its early stages, however, 3D printing technology continues to advance rapidly and offers appealing advantages. *3D printing* allows for the creation of items with complex internal structures that would otherwise be impossible. Standard production procedures like forging and milling necessitate multiple steps in order to generate a flexible wrench. The hex wrench can be 3D printed in a single step if it is more convenient for you.

Designers can preview how the product will look before it's made, which is a big benefit. Since there is no requirement to build the product until after its design has been authorized, there is no risk of producing an item that does not fulfill client expectations.

Because 3D printing demands a high degree of precision in locating the parts that are being produced, it is a drawback of the technology. There is a way to make complex objects with ease using *robotic arms*, but it's difficult to obtain the accuracy needed for that. 3D printing may be better suited to prototypes than mass manufacturing, but there are still numerous companies that employ it for both reasons.

With each passing year, the cost of 3D printing falls. It's projected that 3D printing will become increasingly commonplace in the years to come. Growth in many businesses will be fueled by the greater capacity to produce customized items. You'll find the technology being used for everything from automobiles to aircraft to medicine.

As a result of 3D printing, producers will have to rethink how they approach their work. With this technology, the design process is made much more efficient because designers are able to be a lot more involved. Prototypes and small batches of customized products are particularly susceptible to these issues.

The Production of Local Products

As a result, the supply chain and logistics may be dramatically altered by using 3D printing to make goods closer to the point of sale. As an alternative to having all of its products shipped from a single facility, companies can establish multiple smaller manufacturing facilities around the service area. When it comes to multinational corporations, this is a significant benefit. If you create smaller batches at strategically located sites, the logistics costs can be drastically lowered.

3-D printing can be used for rapid prototyping, short-run production, and rapid customisation of products, in addition to lowering their costs and streamlining logistics.

This would allow for the production of small batches of unique products with a high degree of precision. People will also be able to personalize their own products as a result of this change.

However, 3D printing isn't only about making physical products. In the last few years, technology has been used in everything from health to food to architecture to even art. A few years ago, a medical company created a prosthetic hand for amputees using a 3D printer.

Due to 3D printing's increased efficiency, customers will be able to purchase more customized products. Instead of outsourcing, local manufacturing will bring manufacturing back to the **United States**. To put it another way, 3D printing has the potential to revolutionize the manufacturing industry across **America and Great Britain**, something that this publication's economists can't even begin to contemplate.

<u>3D printing has the potential to fundamentally alter the way we generate and provide healthcare.</u> As 3D printing can manufacture living tissue, it will allow medical experts to construct tailored, functional prostheses for patients. Unlike traditional *prostheses*, these *prosthetics* can be custom-made for each patient and are more accurate. A 3D-printed organ for transplantation could potentially be possible. Dental implants and other medical equipment will benefit greatly from the capacity to print out unique pieces, as well.

Before 3D printing, technology had the ability to transform the manufacturing sector. It is necessary to first create mass manufacturing before it can occur. As 3D printing advances, consumers may soon be able to design and print their own products instead of purchasing them from retailers.

Finding the right 3D Printer

The days of 3D printing being used primarily for prototyping are long gone. Today, 3D printing is becoming increasingly popular and taking action as the technology continues to improve at a steady pace. Now, it can supply adequate advantages from the initial design to the final output.

A few years ago, only a handful of skilled design technical engineers could enjoy the wonderful luxury of in-house printing, as the technology was still developing and confined to a small number of prototypes.

At this point, a large number of amateurs and creative minds have mastered 3D printing, allowing them to unleash their ideas on everyone else in the world. People can now design and print their own models at home.

How can a 3D printer be put to use?

By having your own 3D printer at home, you may be able to make practically any type of 3D object for both personal and professional purposes.

Using a heating device that melts the filament, each layer of a desktop 3D inkjet printer can be created at the same time. The introduction of desktop 3D printers meant that you no longer had to rely on 3D printing firms to produce your design models or prototypes. The price of 3D printers has rapidly decreased, making them more accessible to amateurs and household users alike.

Create your own set of tools, or print a vase exactly as you want it. The possibilities are truly endless. Even if you break something accidentally, you don't have to buy a whole new set of parts to fix it; just print a part and you're good to go!

What to Consider to be a 3D Printing Technology Adopter?

To get the most out of your 3D printer, you'll need to be clear on what you want it to be able to do and what your limitations are. This is the first stage in the process of purchasing a 3D inkjet printer.

A large number of technologically adept technology enthusiasts attempt to build their own 3D inkjet printer from the ground up from parts they have lying around. To begin with, you'll need some advanced mechanical and software development abilities, but if you're motivated and persistent, you should consider pursuing a career in the 3D printing sector.

3D Printer Kits: 3D inkjet printer kits are another way to obtain a functional (hopefully!) **3D inkjet printer.** All of the components needed to set up an inkjet printer are included in these packages. There is a decent amount of mechanized and development expertise that is required from you. Having this knowledge can help you if you ever need to fix an issue with your computer, because you'll know just where to look.

Getting a pre-assembled machine is the most straightforward and fastest way to get your hands on a 3D printer. There are now ready-to-use desktop 3D printers available from most 3D printing firms. Most printers are delivered to you ready to use when you purchase them (even if the calibration has been done). However, this method is more expensive than the other two options, but it saves you a lot of time and effort in the long run.

What to Consider When Choosing a 3D Printer

It is necessary to conduct a thorough evaluation before purchasing a 3D printer.

When comparing 3D printers, here are a few things to keep in mind:

- System size.
- Cost of product.
- Form of filament.
- Support for clients.
- Customer reviews

The Cost of a Pproduct is an important consideration:
How much time and effort are you willing to put into your pastime?

Many different types of 3D printers exist, and their prices vary based on the features they include. **FDM printers**, for example, are among the most affordable desktop printers on the market. Only $1000 will get you a decent one. Also, the filament they use is pretty inexpensive. Remember that you're new to 3D printing and that you'll make a few mistakes (and waste filament!) before you grasp the gist of things. For the first 10–20 hours or so, you should expect to be frustrated by your inkjet printer's inability to produce high-quality prints. Be prepared to waste a lot of filament as well.

There are a wide variety of low-cost filaments available, so it makes sense to look into getting a printer that supports both. Set a budget that just covers the printer purchase before you even begin your search. Element in that you will first save a significant amount of filament before seeing a significant return on your investment.

The Size of the System:

The print surface is another name for the region where the building platform is located. To hold on to something while being imprinted, the abdominal muscle material latches onto a *"breadboard"* with microscopic pores. Warmed printing platforms are now the norm in the industry.

You'll be able to print larger objects and models if you have a larger print area!

Form of Filament:

ABS and **PLA** are the only fibers that desktop printers can print with at the moment. In the previous part, we went into great detail about the various features of the two materials. If you're still unsure, it's a good idea to go back and review the material in question. Many printers should come with spools that are compatible with any reel of filament, allowing you to use any filament you like. That's not the case with the 3D Systems **Codify Cube**, though. Only *Cubify ink cartridges* are needed for this printer.

As long as you're not printing with a **Cubify printer**, you shouldn't have any problems using different types of filament. A kilo of filament from **PLA** can cost anywhere from $30 to $50, depending on the quality.

Also keep in mind that the initial expenditure of 3D printing is not due to material costs but rather to how long an inkjet printer needs to produce a single piece of plastic to complete one model. When it comes to both time and electricity, it all adds up.

Customer Reviews:

Before making a purchase, read the reviews of the 3D printers that pique your interest. You'll need to know the ins and outs of the inkjet printer, which can be revealed through a thorough examination. Comparative investigation of the machines can be done using popular review websites and retail stores.

Ask for honest opinions about inkjet printers on community sites like **Reddit** or **Yahoo Answers**.

Support for Clients:

As a newcomer to the world of *3D printing*, you are likely to encounter difficulties. A child's teething difficulties and 3D printing are connected. It is critical that the company from which you purchase your inkjet printer delivers exceptional customer service. You may learn more about them by reading online reviews and conversing with other people who have used them in the past.

Almost all companies that sell and promote 3D printers provide excellent customer service because they want to encourage the widespread use of 3D printing technology.

Summary

3D printing is experiencing a resurgence akin to that of computing in the 1970s. **3D printing** allows for the creation of items with complex internal structures that would otherwise be impossible. This technology has a wide range of applications and is frequently used in education, as we have seen in previous chapters. 3-D printing can be used for rapid prototyping, short-run production, and rapid customisation of products. Local manufacturing will bring manufacturing back to the U.S. and Great Britain.

3D printing has the potential to revolutionize the manufacturing industry across America and UK. 3D printing has the potential to fundamentally alter the way we generate and provide healthcare. Consumers may soon be able to design and print their own products instead of purchasing them from retailers. The price of 3D printers has rapidly decreased making them more accessible to amateurs and household users alike. A large number of technologically adept technology enthusiasts attempt to build their own 3D inkjet printer.

Getting a pre-assembled machine is the most straightforward and fastest way to get your hands on a 3D printer. There are now ready-to-use desktop 3D printers available from most 3D printing firms. Many different types of 3D printers exist, and prices vary based on the features they include. FDM printers, for example, are among the most affordable desktop printers on the market. ABS and PLA are the only fibers that desktop printers can print with at the moment.

Many printers come with spools that are compatible with any reel of filament, allowing you to use any filament you like. A kilo of PLA can cost anywhere from $30 to $50, depending on the quality. Ask for honest opinions about inkjet printers on community sites like Reddit or Yahoo Answers.

Chapter 3

The Different 3D Printing Processes

The term "3D printing" refers to the process of creating anything from the ground up. There are a variety of techniques that can be employed to achieve this goal.

When it comes to 3D printing, no matter what process is utilized, the fundamentals remain the same, starting with the creation of a computer-aided design (CAD) model and ending with the fabrication of a 3D printing device. However, the actual method by which the physical thing is created varies.

To begin with, there are four main types of 3D printing techniques that you're more likely to come across:

- Stereolithography (SLA)
- Selective Laser Sintering (SLS)
- Fused Deposition Modeling (FDM)
- Multi-Jet Modeling (MJM)

Multi-Jet Modelling (MJM)

Inkjet printers and 3D printers have a lot in common when it comes to their operating principles. **Thermojet** is a common name for this method. Models made of wax-like plastic material can be created using this procedure.

The way it works

There are several straight lines in the mind of the **MJM** printer that spray glue-like material over a powder coating of natural resin. Due to the fact that 3D printing isn't constrained by the same limitations as **SLA**, it can make incredibly intricate things with a width as small as 16 microns. SLA-based models, on the other hand, are more complex to make.

<u>The printer can create a wax-like 3D object layer by layer</u> like this.

A **3D model in STL** format is required for all kinds of 3D printing processes to grasp the blueprints they need to produce, regardless of the type of **3D printing method**.

Layer by layer, all 3D printers construct products from recycled materials; the main variation is in the method of solidifying the recyclables used, as well as the type of recyclables used. A **UV laser beam** is used to cure the materials (which are in a liquified state), whereas SLS uses the laser light to solidify the raw material, which is in a powdered state. Each type has its own set of advantages for a variety of different uses. Some are simple enough to be used in the home or office, but their industrial applications now limit some of these products.

However, the rapid advancements in all 3D printing techniques are making them more accessible to hobbyists and consumers alike.

Stereolithography

Stereolithography is a **process that uses a 3D (SLA) model**. ***Stereolithography***, a 3D printing technology, is widely considered to be the precursor to most other 3D printing processes. 3D systems were pioneered by *Charles W. Hull*, who launched and patented this method in 1988. Using a vat of liquid photopolymer resin, a UV laser beam is used to cure the resin. The laser light hardens the resin coating layer by layer, allowing for the creation of the finished product.

Its functions

To begin with, a SLA 3D inkjet printer uses a lot of water-based plastic. A few pieces of this plastic substance are fused together to produce a three-dimensional item.

SLA printers are made up of four major components:

- Liquid plastic was poured into a printer.
- A platform with holes drilled into it.

A laser with a UV wavelength.

Laser beam and platform control through a personal computer.

Above the system, a very thin layer of plastic material (0.05-0.15mm thick) is exposed. The thing's design is "pulled" across the system by the laser light, as shown in the look files. During the laser etching process, the materials become more durable. This method is used before the object is completed.

If you use SLA to make something, you may expect it to have a smooth surface because it depends on the difficulty level of the SLA machine.

Fused Deposition Modelling (FDM)

Deposition of the Fused Model printing is an additive manufacturing process that can be used for modeling, prototyping, and manufacturing. Coating creates an object-level in this technique as well. Although there are certain variances in how this technology utilizes the materials, it is still an effective method.

The way it works

Using the **FDM method**, 3D printers create object-level layers by heating the material to a semi-liquid state. Support and modeling materials are used by **FDM** in order to complete printing. While the latter serves as a framework, the former serves as the final product.

The printer's bays supply the recyclables, and the printer head is designed to move based on X and Y coordinates that are controlled by the computer. In order for the Z-axis approach to work, a coating must have been applied first.

A clean and simple-to-use technology like **FDM** is suitable for usage in the workplace because of its many advantages.

Selective Laser Sintering (SLS)

SLS is a widely used 3D printing technology. SLS printing uses a high-power laser beam to fuse together small particles of ceramic, cup, or plastic material. Infusing these particles with heat from the laser light, the result is a

3D object.

In the 1980s, Carl Deckard, an undergraduate student at the University of Texas, and his professor, Joe Beaman, invented and copyrighted this method.

The way it works

Once the CAD software has been used to create a 3D model, the SLS machine is used to fabricate the object. 3D printers are able to recognize the STL format from these documents.

Nylon and other common polymers are used in the SLS printing process. For example, a computer controls a laser beam to trace a cross-section of an object onto natural material in order to create that object (natural powder).

The laser's heat is increased until the particles' boiling point is reached, or just below it. The 3D inkjet printer's system descends by 0.1mm to disclose a fresh layer of natural powder after creating the initial level of the object. The object is built layer by layer, and it must cool before being removed from the inkjet printer.

A Collection of STL Files

The *STL file format* is the most commonly used for extending 3D printers. 3D Systems' Stereo Lithography CAD software and tools are believed to have been used to manufacture the extendable.

When it comes to naming a file type, there are a number of possibilities. "Standard Tessellation" refers to the tiling or layering of geometric patterns and designs.

What is the STL Extendable?

The STL extensible can be described as a triangular representation of a 3D object, which is a simple description. If you look closely at the image, you'll notice that the circles in the *CAD model* are represented by simple lines, whereas the triangles in the *STL sketch* represent the group's apex.

The circle seems to be a group in the CAD file, but in the STL version, a succession of triangles is used to fill in the blanks and make it printable on most 3D printers, as shown in the image. Since it is not solid, but rather a mesh of triangles, you'll often hear people refer to or describe 3D inkjet printer drawings as mesh documents.

The STL file format is used by 3D printers. AutoCAD, Solid Works, and Pro/Engineer (now PTC Creo Parametric) are just a few of the many 3D applications that can generate STL files natively or via add-on tools.

In addition to STL, there are a number of additional popular 3D printing document formats from which to choose. OBJ, AMF, PLY, and WRL are all included. Free STL visitors are available for anyone who does not need to pull or generate an STL document.

An STL File is Created

CAD software allows you to save a large portion of your model as an **STL** file once you've finished designing it. Depending on the program you are using and the task you are working on, the **STL document** option may not be visible until you save the file. **STL** extensible meshes the top of your sketch into a mesh of triangles once again.

An item is normally returned to a mesh model when a 3D check is performed, such as with a laser beam scanning device or some digital imaging device. This is not the case when the object is drawn from scratch in **3D modeling software.**

The majority of this is made simple by CAD software, which performs the changes on the fly. In contrast to this, some 3D modeling tools allow you to fine-tune the number and size of triangles in your mesh, which might result in a denser or more complicated mesh surface and thus a better 3D printer. In order to get the greatest STL file, you don't need to know the ins and outs of every 3D modeling program.

Deviation/Chordal Tolerance

A tessellated (layered or tiled) triangle's distance from the original sketching surface is called a "pixel distance."

The ability to control the angle at which the camera is

The print resolution can be improved by creating gaps between neighboring triangles and varying the angle of deviation between them. This means that the weld between the two triangle surfaces is substantially stronger as a result. As a result of this, you can increase the distance between things that are split or tiled together (standard tessellation).

Binary or ASCII?

It is easier to distribute binary files because they are smaller and easier to post and download. A benefit of ASCII papers is that they are easier to read and verify visually.

Visit **Stratasys Direct Manufacturing's** on how to prepare STL files article for a fast overview of how to do this in software.

What Makes an STL File Bad?

The two most important guidelines for a good STL document are as follows: <u>The first rule states that adjacent triangles must have two vertices that are the same distance apart. The vertices and normals of the triangles must be aligned in order for the triangles' orientation to be consistent.</u> Problems can be detected in the STL document if any of the two conditions is not met.

Summary

There are four main types of 3D printing techniques that you're more likely to come across. Each type has its own set of advantages for a variety of different uses. The fundamentals remain the same, but the actual method by which the physical thing is created varies. Stereolithography is the precursor to most other 3D printing processes. Using a vat of liquid photopolymer resin, a UV laser beam cures it layer by layer.

Fused Deposition Modelling (FDM) creates an object-level layer in this technique. SLS printing uses a high-power laser beam to fuse together small particles of ceramic, cup, or plastic. 3D printers are able to recognize the STL format from these documents. The STL extensible can be described as a triangular representation of a 3D object. The STL file format is used by 3D printers.

AutoCAD, Solid Works, and Pro/Engineer are just a few of the many 3D applications that can generate STL files natively or via add-on tools. Free STL visitors are available for anyone who does not need to pull or generate an STL document. Some 3D modeling tools allow you to fine-tune the number and size of triangles in your mesh. This might result in a denser or more complicated mesh surface for a better 3D printer. The ability to control the angle at which the camera is pointed can also improve print resolution.

Chapter 4

Maintenance of a 3D printer and its Filament

A **3D inkjet printer**, like any other piece of equipment, requires routine maintenance and care in order to function well. To keep your **3D printer** in peak condition, you must perform a number of routine maintenance tasks.

Plastic filament, the raw material for printing, represents the lineage of a printer. You can't produce anything if you don't have enough of this filament. If the quality of your filament begins to deteriorate, your finished products' quality may drop significantly.

Having the correct 3D printer filament on hand is therefore critical.

What do you mean by the term "filaments"?

Polylactic acid (PLA) is the most commonly used filament in 3D printers. Corn starch and water are used to create this substance. For **FDM printers**, this is the most common filament, while for 3D printers, it is one of the most popular options. **PLA filament** can be purchased in a variety of colors and finishes. It might have a high or low molecular weight, depending on its use.

Is there a good reason to use filaments?

A 3D printer's filament is a must. There would be no prints if it wasn't there. Amazon is one of the places where you can buy filament online.

We'll go into great detail on how to properly maintain and store 3D printer filament in this section.

Recommendations on How to Care for Your 3D Printer

A well-maintained 3D printer will last for many years while providing you with perfect service and delivering images of the highest quality.

The following tips will help you keep your printer in the best possible condition.

1. Always use the recommended filament and filament holder.

2. Ensure that your filament spool is always firmly seated in its holder and that the spool is not damaged or worn.

3. When using a heated bed, ensure that it is clean and dry.

4. Do not use any lubricants or other materials that might damage the printer.

5. Clean the extruder gear with a cloth dampened with rubbing alcohol. Wipe the gear in a circular motion until it appears clean.

6. Make sure the filament spool is not blocking the nozzle opening.

Among other recommendations are;

The Rods should be Lubricated:

In order to move the extruder head, we use the X, Y, and Z axis. Effortless movement is essential for a finished product that is the most accurate you can make it. The reason for this is that after cleaning up any residue on your X, Y, and Z rods, you should lubricate each one. Monthly is a good starting point. With your Z rod in place, you need to add some grease to the top of the Z rod. It does not matter how much grease you put on; just make sure you get it all. Now, you can move your extruder head and extrude your filament. After the filament is extruded, it needs to be cleaned. To clean the filament, turn off your hotend.

Get the Nuts and Bolts Snug:

To allow for movement, the 3D printer's mechanism was designed to be prone to loosening its nuts and bolts over time. Using a printer if the rollers are too loose will cause it to shake, reducing accuracy significantly. For the rest of the year, tighten all of the bolts and nuts once a month. Never over-tighten the screws.

Print the Frame:

To make sure that the printer will remain stable, print the frame with a 0.15mm layer height, which will produce a frame of 1mm thickness. Print the frame with a 100% infill, which means that every single filament will be used to fill in the gaps between the 3D-printed pieces. 3D print the front plate of the frame. Make sure that you do not use any filaments thinner than 2.15mm for this print. Fill the frame with PLA: 3D print the back plate of the frame. This time, use a 3.15mm filament. As the printed parts are thin, they may warp slightly.

Change the Belt Tension if needed:

The belt pressure can be checked to make sure it's correct without causing any damage. The quality of a printout will suffer if the right tension is not maintained. You can change the level of tension as needed. For detailed instructions on adjusting the tension on your printer's belt, consult the device's user manual.

Ensure that the Extruder Gear is Flossed:

Small pieces of plastic can build up in the extruder gear over time, preventing it from rotating normally. Use a pointy object (such as a toothpick) to clean out the gear's tooth of any debris.

Consider Updating Your Software:

When it comes to inkjet printer maintenance, it's not just about fixing the printer's hardware. Make sure you're always on the lookout for ways to make your extruder even better! 3D printer firmware has improved significantly over the last few years and will continue to do so in the future as well.

If you use a software program to control the printer, you must update it as soon as a new version is released. The newer versions may have eliminated a large number of bugs and errors.

If necessary, Build Areas can be Replaced:

It is imperative that you replace your building surfaces if they become warped in order to achieve the perfect toned build.

You need to be aware of just a few of these things. You should always consult the owner's manual for your specific 3D inkjet printer model for information on how to perform routine maintenance.

If all else fails, you can *"expect the best"* and try to *"manifest a wonder"* with your 3D printing!

Using Your 3D Printer in a Way that is Recommended

Avoid being a Slacker:

We know you'll be thrilled when your 3D printer arrives. You don't have to start using it right away. There is a chance that something will go wrong. Taking it slow and reading the user manual one at a time is the most straightforward method.

Remember the Hot Nozzle:

To melt the filament, the extruder's nozzle must be hot enough. Temperatures can rise to more than 150 degrees

Celsius. Keep in mind that the inkjet printer's nozzle is likely to be very hot during printing, and you don't want a small indentation in the printer bed!

Do not assume that it has been Calibrated properly:
Despite the fact that printers are now pre-calibrated, things can change when they are shipped. Verify the following to make sure everything is in order:

- Clearance of the printing bed from the nozzle;
- correct software configuration of the printer;
- properly loaded print bed sizes.

When and Where to Keep Printer Filament

Even if it's made of wood, ceramic, or any other type of material, water will seep into it.

When it comes to commonly used **3D printing filaments**, **ABS** and **PLA** both have water absorption properties. Their quality is significantly diminished if they are allowed to absorb moisture.

The filaments will absorb moisture, resulting in the formation of small water bubbles, necessitating adequate storage space. Bubbles may form in the filament as it is heated during the printing process, causing the materials to be spewed rather than laid down precisely.

PLA cartridges and ***spools*** are also known to become brittle if they are exposed to a lot of moisture. A lot of people have noticed this after their filament snapped while being prepared by the extruder.

Store in airtight plastic bags and containers is the best way to keep moisture out of the filaments.

Custom cases for the *PLS filament reels and spools* are always an option if you prefer. As an alternative, you can keep your feedstock dry by using a ***dehumidifier***.

Plastic filament reels can be stored in an airtight plastic container. Use uncooked grain as a desiccant to ensure that your plastic filaments are perfectly dry!

You can use a dryer to remove the moisture from **ABS**, but you can't dry **PLA**, so it won't be able to absorb dampness. Vacuum-sealed kits with desiccants are sent out by nearly every reputable manufacturer of plastic filaments. When desiccants are in a closed system, they are at their most efficient. You should only use the pack if you absolutely have to. Use a plastic handbag to store it after use, and place a few desiccants inside to absorb any moisture.

Summary

Having the correct 3D printer filament on hand is critical to ensuring a high-quality print. Polylactic acid (PLA) is the most commonly used filament in 3D printers. Amazon is one of the places where you can buy filament online for printing and other purposes. The 3D printer's mechanism was designed to be prone to loosening its nuts and bolts over time. After the filament is extruded, it needs to be cleaned before it can be moved by hand.

Use a pointy object (such as a toothpick) to clean out the gear. If you use a software program to control the printer, you must update it as soon as a new version is released. The nozzle is likely to be very hot during printing, and you don't want a small indentation in the printer bed! Do not assume that it has been calibrated properly. PLA cartridges and spools can become brittle if they are exposed to a lot of moisture.

Use uncooked grain as a desiccant to ensure that your plastic filaments are perfectly dry after use. The best way to keep your feedstock dry is by using a dehumidifier.

Chapter 5

3D Printer Structural Elements Removal

You'll tumble if you lean too far to one side. That is a law of physics, and it's a matter of course. You might not think about it when you start working with a **3D inkjet printer**. Overhanging or protruding parts, such as an outstretched arm, a brimmed cap, or the space between two points, require you to rediscover the laws and regulations of physics and gravity when you attempt to print them.

3D printing frequently needs assistance. In order to prevent it from falling over, sagging, or melting, any object that has an overhang or is otherwise not a simple form must have some sort of structural support component.

This is where your printer becomes a workhorse. To remove overhangs and other structural components, follow these guidelines:

- Always start at the top.
- The first step in removing overhangs is to print a test run. If you don't, you can end up with a partially printed model that falls apart, or worse yet, an entire

print job that doesn't print at all.

- **Use supports:** A support is a thin plate that extends from one layer to another. Supports are useful for many reasons, but they're especially useful for overhangs. They allow you to build large, complex models without having to print one part at a time. Support plates can be printed at the same time as your model, and they're easy to remove and add as your model changes.

Adding 3D Printing Helpers

When creating a model in a **CAD application**, help can be supplied manually, in the repair stage using specialized software, or in the printing stage using slicing software. 3D professionals commonly recommend **Simplify 3D** as a highly effective tool for increasing facilities, which is a commercial program. For those on a tight budget, **Meshmixer** and **Netfabb** are good freeware solutions.

How to Remove a Support in 3D Printing

Support materials can be removed in a different manner by

most **3D printing** enthusiasts.

Most of the support materials can be broken away with your hands in situations like this. Remove the rest of the support with needle-nose pliers or a putty blade sharpened on one side. Time and a steady hand are all that are needed for this technique.

Using a 3D printer with two extruders allows you to use a standard **PLA** or **ABS** material for one extruder and a lower-density support material for the other, which makes support removal much easier. In most cases, a chemical substance, water shower, will dissolve the support material. This process is offered by the **Stratasys Mojo 3D inkjet printer**, which is nice, but out of reach for the average consumer hobbyist.

With a *3D printing service bureau*, you can choose the level of finish you want for your object, or purchase a finished product and have it finished by someone else if you prefer.

In some cases, a support is not completely attached to the object and it can be removed with the least amount of effort. This technique is called **"punching"** and the support is punched away with a sharpened tool.

Punching is the most common method of removing supports in 3D printing, but is not always the most effective way. This is the most common technique used to remove supports from an object. The sharpened tool is pressed into the support material, which causes it to break away. This is a very effective way of removing supports from **3D prints**, but it can be a little time consuming.
The following steps show you how to do this technique.

Get the Right Tool for the Job Use a tool that has a sharpened edge, such as a putty blade or a razor.

This will give you a sharper punch and allow you to make multiple cuts. Keep in mind that the sharp edge of the tool may dull over time, so sharpen it if needed. Remove Supports When you have finished punching all of your supports, take a moment to inspect your print. If there are any cracks or areas where the support was not completely removed, use a fine-toothed screwdriver to try to pry them away. If the support material does not come off, then you will need to find a different way to remove it.

Removing Supports Without Punches

There are times when you want to remove supports from an object without using a punch. In this case, you will need to cut the support material away. You may be able to do this with a sharp knife, but it may be more effective to use a cutting tool. The following steps show you how to remove supports without using a punch.

Cutting a Support

1. Remove any objects or surfaces that might interfere with your cutting tool.

2. If possible, cut through the center of the support material. This will make it easier to remove the material later.

3. Use a utility knife to cut a straight line across the bottom edge of the support. Cut all the way through the support material, but stop before you reach the surface of the object you are removing supports from.

Methods for Getting Rid of 3D Support

The following suggestions should be kept in mind when exploring the best ways to remove **3D-printed models'** facilities:

To make slicing easier when using a blade or scratch, heat the model or the knife. A small butane torch may be useful, but exercise caution when using it to protect your model. As far as I'm concerned, it works like a champ. With high-grit sandpaper ranging from 220 to 1200, damp sanding removes the model's support framework and polishes it.

In the case of **PLA materials**, stress marks can be seen where the model's support materials meet the model itself. Nail polish varnish can be used to repair scratches and dings if this happens to you.

Using a **Dremel** to operate your **3D printing** shop like a dentist's office is a great way to get started. To make removing support materials as simple as possible, these handheld grinders come with a range of parts and accessories. If you don't have rock-solid grip strength, use extreme caution when machining your fragile plastic creations.

Changing 3D Printer Speed and Heating Settings

The 3D Inkjet printer settings just require a small amount of heat and speed adjustment.

Helpful tidbits:

For those who don't want to tinker with their printers themselves, a simple trick is to use two extruders, one for the model and one to extrude a raft. For each extruder, a purge wall structure is set up to wipe away any excess filament that has been extruded, resulting in a chilling of model levels and a slowing of the printing speed.

It is possible to use two different **FFF settings.**

There will be a 90% infill for the call box and four perimeter outlines for the top, which will be filled in with 10% infill, and two shells for the spire. When building a thicker foundation, this will help keep it from falling over. One **FFF configuration** will be built for each region in **Simplify 3D**.

Make it easier to manage 3D settings for different areas:

The first step is to establish where the transition from 90% to 10% should take place, immediately below the windows' highest level. Simplify 3D's Mix Section Tool can be used to break apart a model, allowing a user to see into the model's structure. In order to trim the model slightly below the top windowpane, move the slider along the Z-plane axis. Make a note of this number.

Extrusion settings can be changed by creating a new region:

First, start a new FFF process to specify the lowest parameters, and then build a new FFF process to configure the highest values.

Perimeter settings for your 3D model can be changed:

Afterwards, go to the Layer tab and modify the Outer Perimeter Shells from 2 to 4 under the Layers section. However, infill settings may change from time to time.

Changing the perimeter settings:

The next step is to increase the infill on the infill tabs to 90%.

Changing Print Job Preferences for Different Areas:

In the Advanced tabs, select which layers to apply this approach to. The 18mm level, previously determined to be the lowest level for the bottom.

Click Okay to save many of the options because of the procedure of setting them at the bottom. Printing from 18mm to the highest quality on advanced-level tabs requires a new procedure that uses a different shell thickness of 2, a higher infill percentage of 10%, and a different region of printing that uses a different infill thickness of 10%. You must click OK to save the second process's configurations before continuing.

Time to print off the advanced slicing settings for future reference:

The model is ready to be printed after both methods have been developed. When the Select Process for *Printing home window displays*, select **"Go"** for all to employ both setups when preparing to print.

In order to get an idea of how the model will look, it is always a good idea to perform the preview printing first. Other aspects that can be customized for individual printing include a lot of pondering and head-scratching, as well as learning from your mistakes and bad prints. In spite of this, **FDM/FFF printers** are capable of printing and making a wide variety of interesting things with the right planning, preparation, design, mesh repair, and printing configurations.

Summary

Overhanging or protruding parts, such as an outstretched arm, a brimmed cap, or the space between two points, require you to rediscover the laws of physics and gravity when you attempt to print them. To remove overhangs and other structural components, follow these guidelines.

Using a **3D printer** with two extruders allows you to use a standard **PLA** or **ABS** material for one extruder and a lower-density support material for the other. Cutting, sanding, and polishing are some of the best ways to remove *3D-printed models'* support. A small butane torch may be useful, but exercise caution when using it to protect your model.

The **Dremel** can be used to operate your **3D printing** shop like a dentist's office. **Simplify 3D's Mix Section Tool** can be used to break apart a model, allowing a user to see into the model's structure. Make a note of where the transition from **90% to 10%** infill should take place below the windows' highest level.

Chapter 6

Important software for 3D printers

3D printing would remain a pipe dream if the proper software weren't available. Despite the fact that you'll need a **3D printer**, you'll also need a variety of vital tools to produce the model and convert it to a format that the printer can recognize.

In this chapter, you'll learn about the finest software for completing these duties. **3D design software:** To begin, you'll need a **3D modeling program**. Aside from **CAD applications**, there are a number of additional programs that can be used to build **3D models**.

The following are two of the most frequently encountered kinds of:

Parametric modeling software is the first type. These apps allow you to create complicated designs by altering a sequence of simple shapes. Autodesk's Inventor is a good example of this type of software.

Another sort of 3D modeling software is called **CAD (computer-aided design)**. These are specialized 3D design programs that allow you to create precise 3D models of products. The use of **CAD software** is highly recommended when it comes to creating designs and blueprints for construction projects. They're commonly used by architects, engineers, and other professionals who need accurate measurements and technical specifications for their work.

A 3D design program is perfect for making printable 3D models, such as jewelry and figurines. They can also be used to build animated 3D objects that respond to touch. You can use a mix of CAD and 3D design programs to create a 3D model, which can then be converted into a format that a 3D printer can use. 3D printer simulators are useful if you want to make sure your project is compatible with your printer before printing it out.

The first step for a 3D printing specialist is to familiarize themselves with the many software options available.

Getting Started with 3D Printing

If you're not going to use pre-made **3D printing software**, you'll need to know what kind of software you'll need if you want to print objects. The first thing you need to do is choose the type of 3D printer that you have in mind. Then, you can begin looking for a specific software program that will help you to create your object.

An Overview of 3D Printing

Before we get deeper into discussing **3D printing software**, it is a wise idea to briefly cover the actual 3D printing process from scratch, so you have a definite sense of just what you're working with.

In the first step, you need to come up with a concept.
First and foremost, decide on what you want to create. From a simple piece of furniture to a more complex piece of art, it could be anything. It's best to start with easy chores before moving on to more complex ones. Using a 3D printer for the first time, we began by printing cubes and other simple shapes.

Additionally, it's crucial to do so at this time. When it comes to **3D printing**, it's easy to become bogged down in brainstorming new inventions, but don't let yourself get carried away. If you're prone to procrastinating on your projects, you might want to check out these helpful tips on how to stop.

Next, you should print a small robot and an ice cream cone. Now that you know what you want to print, the next step is finding a design that you like. It should be something that's not too hard to replicate, but still looks unique and cool. If you're working with a team, have everyone involved in the project sign off on the final design. Once you have your design, it's time to move on to the next step: creating your 3D model.

Second Step 2: Create the Model

Developing a genuine model is the first major stage in the process. **CAD software (or non-CAD software)** is needed to assist you in creating the model once you've decided what you want to produce. It's not an easy task to learn how to use a specific design software, and you should be prepared for this and willing to learn.

There are a number of excellent tutorials on the **3D Insider YouTube channel** that demonstrate the basics of common CAD tools, including **Autodesk Inventor.**

Converting it into STL is the third step.

Following the completion of your model, it is imperative that you convert it to **STL**. The ability to export a **CAD model** as an **STL file** is integrated into many of the CAD programs you will come across throughout your career. If you're going to use **non-CAD design software** like **Google Sketch Up**, you'll need to set up a plugin (in this example, **Cad Span**) to be able to alter and convert the final design.

An **STL file** is a file format that contains the information needed to create a **3D model** using *stereolithography printers.*

To export your design as an **STL file**, you will need to find a CAD program that has this capability built in. The process of exporting your model to an STL file is fairly simple, and involves just a few steps. Download **FreeCAD**; a powerful, open-source CAD program. It's free to download, install, and use.

You're only halfway through the process of creating a 3D printable file when you convert your model to *STL format*.

Slice it up.

In order to complete the fourth phase, you must slice the model into sections. It is therefore possible to teach a **3D**

printer the process of making the object. Inkjet printers can recognize the final **G-code document** as a result of this final step in the use of software applications.

You will need software to generate the model, convert it into **STL**, and slice the model for the **3D inkjet printer** as well.

Slicer and Printer-control Apps

Slicing and transmitting are two additional stages that your model goes through as it learns to become a finished result. By *slicing*, the model is divided into multiple printed levels, with tool paths drawn to each level. These instructions are transmitted to the inkjet printer, which subsequently produces an object-level layer by layer.

The majority of **3D printers** can be operated either with an inbuilt display or via a USB connection to a computer. **Control software** (*which may be the slicer software*) communicates with the inkjet printer via this interface, which manages major criteria like acceleration, circulation, and the heat necessary for each layer.

Slicer and control software functions are combined in the **Netfabb engine**, for example. There are, however, a number of different types of slicers, as well as different types of control software.

Slic3r

It's possible to use Slic3r, a well-known tool, to turn an electronic 3D model into printing instructions for a 3D printer with sophisticated features. An extruding tool path can be generated by slicing the model into layers and calculating the extruded materials.

Starting from a blank slate in 2011, the project has since grown into an application that is supported by nearly every major 3D printing company in the world. In order for Slic3r to function as a controller app, it requires additional software.

These applications are included in the package:

- Pronterface
- Replicant Host
- The G Replicator

For those who are new to the field of 3D printing, a comprehensive manual may be found at https://manual.slic3r.org/.

Skeinforge

In addition to **RapMan** and other **Fab laboratory motors**, **Skeinforge** was designed to be used in conjunction with this slicer application. As a novice user, you may be better off with a simpler tool because this program has a lot of options for setting parameters, but the learning curve is steep.

Kisslicer

An Inkjet printer **G Code** can be generated from an **STL file** using **KiSSlicer**, an easy-to-use application. With a single-head 3D inkjet printer, the free edition of **KISSlicer** provides all the functions needed. The **PRO version** may be necessary if you need to print with several heads and multiple models.

Summary

It doesn't matter which program you use; remember that you'll need to master multiple things, and even the simplest programs have a steep learning curve. If you've never worked with **3D development** before, this will take a lot of time and effort on your behalf. Many programs come with lengthy documentation that needs to be studied in order to fully grasp the basic operations and layout of the settings.

To save money on costly software, wait until you're confident in your design for **3D development** and printing before moving on to free software.

In this chapter, you'll learn about the finest software for **3D printing**. Parametric modeling software allows you to create complicated designs by altering a sequence of simple shapes. **Autodesk's Inventor** is a good example of this type of software. The use of **CAD software** is highly recommended when it comes to creating designs and blueprints for construction projects. When it comes to **3D printing**, it's easy to become bogged down in brainstorming new inventions, but don't get carried away.

Developing a genuine model is the first major stage in the process. **CAD software** (*or non-CAD software*) is needed to assist you in creating the model once you've decided what you want to produce. There are a number of excellent tutorials on the **3D Insider YouTube channel** that demonstrate the basics of common CAD tools like

Autodesk Inventor. To export a **CAD model** as an **STL file**, you will need a **CAD program** that has this capability built in. Download **FreeCAD**, a powerful, open-source **CAD program** that is free to download, install, and use.

An **STL file** is a file format that contains the information needed to create a 3D model using *stereolithography printers*. You will need software to generate the model, convert it into STL, and slice the model for the 3D inkjet printer as well. **Slic3r** turns an electronic 3D model into printable instructions for a 3D printer. An Inkjet printer **G Code** can be generated from an **STL file** using **KiSSlicer.** With a single-head 3D inkjet printer, the free edition of **KISSlicer** provides all the functions needed.

Chapter 7

Hardware that is critical to 3D printing

If you want to get the most out of **3D printing**, you need to have a deep understanding of the printer's hardware. The gear and software you use must operate together. So, if you don't understand the hardware, you're missing half the equation! The hardware of 3D printers may be tough to comprehend, but the basic purpose of the primary components is much easier to grasp than it appears at first. <u>In this section, we'll take a look at how a 3D inkjet printer works and the other essential components that make up a basic 3D printer.</u>

What Is a 3D Printer?

A 3D printer takes a design as an input and then prints the object it's given, whether that's a physical piece of plastic or a digital file. Some 3D printers can print in metal, glass, ceramic, and even wax.

How a 3D Printer Makes a Product

You should already know that a 3D inkjet printer builds objects layer by layer before they are finished. A framework and three axes are included in an inkjet printer:

- The X-axis is (still moving left to right)
- Axis of Y-coordinates (front side to back motion)
- The Z-axis (along with movement).

A part called **an extruder** is installed on the **X-axis** to feed the materials that can be used to create an object. The extruder head is the cheapest part of the **extruder**. As you can see, this is the portion where the filament is melted and "extruded" from a tiny millimeter-sized hole.

The 3D Printer's Physiology

You don't need to know everything about the **3D printer** in order to use it effectively. If you ever need to fix your 3D printer, you'll have a better idea of how to do it if you've studied the basic hardware and construction of one. If you're looking to buy an inkjet printer, this information might be really helpful.

We've previously covered a wide range of 3D printing processes and types. **Fused Deposition Modeling (FDM)** is the most common desktop **3D printing technology**, and this section will focus on it. The *"glue-gun" method* can be compared to this method. The glue-gun approach involves heating a filament to a point where it melts, positioning the melted filament in thin layers, and then setting it up layer-by-layer until the desired thickness is achieved.

Print Bed

It is on this surface that the printer creates the things, *layer by layer*. Based on the filament you are using; you may need to heat the **printing bed.** Painter's tape can be used to cover a non-heated bed.

You must keep the print bed warm during the layering process for heated print mattresses in order to avoid warping. Over the course of the printing process, temperatures range from 40 degrees Celsius to 110 degrees Celsius.

Some printers can reach dangerously high temperatures, and further caution should be taken if children are present. As soon as you touch a warmed-up printing bed, you'll immediately learn your lesson.

Extruder

Many consider the extruder to be the source of plastic

filament expulsion. It's not quite accurate to say that the extruder is just responsible for pulling and feeding filament to the *hot end*.

Hot ends incorporate **extruders**. *Bowden wires* may be used to drive filament to the hot end from a different location, such as a distance from the hot end. When using a dual-extruder inkjet printer, it is possible to print in two different colors and materials simultaneously. An additional extruder and a hot end will be required, which will add to the overall cost.

Hot End

A 3D printer's "hot result" includes a *heater*, a *temperature sensor, and an extrusion tip.* If you don't want to burn yourself, don't even think of fiddling with the hot end of one of these things, which, as the name suggests, can get quite hot. In the nozzle, there are two apertures that range in size from 0.2 mm to 0.8 mm.

The finer the print, the smaller the nozzle of the hot end, but the longer it will take to print the thing.

Plastic Filaments

Although the *plastic filament* is not a part of the inkjet printer, it is a consumable that is necessary for its operation. Like ***inkjet printer cartridges***, you'll be unable to print with your **3D inkjet printer** without **filament**. There are a variety of filaments that may be used **with 3D printing machines**. **ABS** and **PLA** are the two most commonly used materials for home **3D printers**. In the following part, we'll go through both types in great detail.

For printers that employ **Fused Deposition Modeling (FDM),**

ABS compounding in terms of additive manufacturing processes, modeling is perhaps the most common and can be used by the majority of desktop 3D printers.

For FDM printers, filament is fed into the extruder where it is heated to a temperature sufficient to melt it. Extruding the heated filament out of the nozzles, each object is coated simultaneously.

FDM printers have many advantages:

- Compared to other 3D printers, this may be acquired for as little as $1000 to $5000.

- In addition, the filament used in these printers is very reasonably priced.
- A wide range of materials are at their disposal.
- In addition, they are simple to maintain and replace parts.
- They have a quick printing speed.

FDM printers have some drawbacks:
- The nozzles are prone to being blocked.
- Even with help, it can be difficult to completely clean up.
- In the long run, the average person's layers can be seen (striping).

FDM printers can be used to make items made of the following materials:
- Plastic (PLA)
- Made of ABS plastic.

The wood filament is available in two varieties:

Stereolithography (SLA) Printers

Stereolithography is one of the earliest methods of producing additively manufactured goods. These 3D printers utilize a UV light beam to solidify a pool of liquid resin. A new level can be added to an object even before the complete object has been molded, since the base moves to allow for the development of another level.

This 3D printing approach is best suited to those who want their items to have a high level of detail. These printers can cost anything from $3000 to $7000.

There are many advantages to using SLA printers.

- The best products can have exquisite detail down to 25 microns (thicker than a sheet of paper).
- Objects built using this method have a smooth top.
- In addition to casting and molding, this method can also be used to create detailed models.

SLA printers have some drawbacks, such as:

- The nozzles are prone to being blocked.
- The use of water resin may generate a substantial amount of waste.
- Only a restricted number of things can be used.
- They are more fragile materials.
- The cost of these printers is usually higher than that

of FDM machines.

When printing with SLA technology, water resin is the only material that can be used.

Different kinds of printers for beginners

We'll go through the benefits and drawbacks of each type of 3D inkjet printer in this part, as well as other information that will help you make an informed decision. In case you've forgotten, there are three sorts of printers:

- Fused Deposition Modeling Printers (FDM)
- Printers that use stereolithography (SLA)
- Printers that use laser beam sintering (SLS)

Filament Types: PLA or ABS?

For 3D printing, there are countless materials available, from various metals to wood and even chocolate! In terms of plastic material filaments, however, PLA and AB fibers are the most widely used filaments.

Plastic polylactic acidity (PLA), or polylactic acidity (PLA), is a biodegradable plastic substance that has various advantages for 3D printing. For example, it does not typically emit any noxious fumes. It's also shiny, and

PLA-made objects have a slick appearance in terms of appearance. It's tougher than ABS, but it's also more fragile, which doesn't imply it'll snap. In contrast, **PLA** is incredibly durable and is significantly more likely to snap rather than flex because of this.

Acrylonitrile butadiene styrene, or Ab muscles, is a petroleum-based plastic substance. They melt at a higher temperature than **PLA**. It's a very durable material, and it's commonly used to manufacture toys like Lego. When compared to PLA, this filament's products are more prone to bending than snapping.

The similarities and differences between these two filament types will be thoroughly explored in this section. We'll also keep talking about the various filament widths. There are pros and downsides to each material, so you may choose the best one for your project.

Inkjet printers that use selective laser sintering

However, unlike **SLA**, the Selective Laser FU light sintering process uses a natural powder rather than liquid resin. A laser beam is used to warm up the natural powder. This natural powder can then be removed to leave behind a solid object once the creation is completed.

These printers cost more than $50,000 each. If you haven't just won the lottery, this isn't always a viable option! Many online printing services may be used if you wish to print a model out like this.

SLS Printers Have the Following Benefits:

- They have a resolution of 16 microns, which is extremely fine.
- When printing an object, there is no need for any additional support structures.
- Working mechanical elements are possible without the need for assembly.

SLS printers have some drawbacks:

- It only takes a little effort to remove the natural powder that accumulates after printing an object.
- There are no desktop SLS printers at this time.

Using an SLS printer, you may produce items out of the following materials:

- Aluminum.
- Plastics and nylon

- Sandstone.
- Silver
- Steel
- The Known Terrain

Thermal plastics include both ABS and polylactic acid (PLA). Warming them up makes them smooth and pliable. Cooling them makes them rigid. Because of how frequently it may be used, this method has become so popular.

Only a tiny fraction of the total number of thermoplastics on the market are suitable for 3D printing.

Three tests must be passed by a material before it can be used in 3D printing:

- Initiation of Preliminary Plastic Material Extrusion
- Trace-binding and Second Extrusion in 3D Printing
- End-User Software

For the three assessments, materials must be easily converted into a 3D printer feedstock known as *plastic material filament.* The filaments are packaged on a reel. So, the material can form precise parts of the products generated by 3D printers.

The plastic material's properties must also have acceptable traits relating to their strength and gloss, as well as other qualities.

Lastly, the first test involves moving PLA and PLA-based thermoplastics around in a test tube. It's just a matter of cost and the time required to transform the resin into a filament of higher quality.

Storage

In order to keep thermoplastics like ABS and **PLA** from absorbing moisture from the environment, they should be sealed before they are utilized or kept for a lengthy period of time.

But this does not mean that if you let the reel of your filament sit for a week or so before using it, it will always be spoiled. Even so, exposure to the environment for an extended period of time might degrade the quality of the raw materials and the finished item.

To prevent moisture from soaking into the filament, it is coated with plastic. Storage of **ABS** and **PLA** might have a negative impact on the quality of the finished product.

When a person's ABS are exposed to the elements, they absorb moisture, which causes them to bubble and spill out of the nozzle when they are used to print an object. When this happens, you'll notice that the nozzle is more prone to becoming clogged and that the life expectancy will be reduced. Using a food dehydrator, you can dry the **ABS** before using them.

When exposed to moisture, **PLA** reacts in a variety of ways. It is possible to notice various other changes in its properties, including bubbles and spilling out of the nozzle during the printing process.

PLA can depolymerize at high temperatures when it comes into contact with drinking water. **Depolymerization** is the process of breaking down a material into smaller components.

When drying **PLA** using a food dehydrator, keep in mind that the crystallinity percentage will change significantly and that extrusion qualities may also be affected.

However, the majority of 3D printers don't have this issue.

Smells

The scent of hot plastic material is noticeable as the muscles are warmed. This is a little inconvenience for some, but most people don't even notice it. Without appropriate ventilation, it's impossible to tell if you've engaged your ABS or not. Additionally, be sure that the **ABS** you use are free of pollution. For the system materials to be heated to the correct temperature, a reliable extruder plays a crucial role in managing the smell.

PLA, because it is made from sugar, emits a semi-sweet aroma similar to that of cooking food essential oil when heated. It won't bring back memories of those great home-cooked meals, but some feel its stench to be superior to that of **ABS**.

Parts Precision

Using both **ABS** and **PLA**, it is possible to make dimensionally correct parts and products. There are a few more things to consider regarding precision when discussing parts.

The upward curling of the top that is directly connected to your printer's print bed is one of the primary concerns concerning the utilization of **ABS**. Your best bet is to warm up the printing bed before you start printing to ensure it's as smooth and easy as possible. Prior to printing, some individuals believe it is more convenient to use a variety of remedies, such as the ABS/Acetone combination or a basic curly hair aerosol. There has been some success with hair squirts on the printing bed in 3D Insider's experiments (note that hair aerosol is highly combustible).

Circular characteristics, such as transparent corners, are more common. It's possible to use a small fan to cool the area around the nozzle in order to improve these edges, but doing so too much will reduce the adhesion between your layers and eventually cause the final product to split open. In comparison to the ABS, PLA warps substantially less often than PLA. As a result, things could be printed without the use of a warmed bed. Sharper details, such as razor-sharp corners, can be achieved if the material is cooled properly. Airflow can also help by conditioning the object and tying all the levels together more tightly.

Characteristics of Materials in General

No matter how well a part is made, it must be able to carry out its intended functions.

There are a wide variety of **ABS**, and they can be engineered to perform a variety of functions. What you get is a solid plastic substance with modest flexibility. **ABS** are dyed a milky beige color. It is possible to sand and process the materials due to their reasonable adaptability. In addition, it is easier to recycle than **PLA**.

Technicians favor the **ABS** for their strong power, adaptability, and machining ability.

PLA: Sugar beets, corn, and potatoes are the building blocks of **PLA**. Because of this, **PLA** is considered to be more environmentally friendly than **ABS**. It is common practice to package food and to construct food storage containers. Originally, it was transparent but can be tinted in a variety of ways to provide variable degrees of opacity and transparency.

It's a lot more powerful and stiff than ABS. PLA-printed products have a bright appearance and a clean feel. However, because of its intricate interlocking setup and pin-joints, it is a little more difficult to use.

Filament Thickness

1.75 mm and 3 mm PLA filaments are available for ABS and PLA filaments, respectively.

Each *extruder* in an inkjet printer is designed to use a specific thickness of filament. You'll need to look at your printer's specifications to see which filament you may use with your **3D printer model**.

In some cases, printers are designed to employ proprietary diameters, which may differ somewhat from the standard thickness. Choose an inkjet printer that supports standard diameters, so you may choose a plastic material filament provider with a wider range of color and material possibilities. This is especially useful for those who haven't purchased an inkjet printer yet.

Filament diameter varies significantly from one

manufacturer to another, too. However, if a filament is referred to as 3 mm, it should never exceed that value; it can, however, be substantially less than 3 mm (say, 2.88 mm).

Some filaments can also include bumps and throats that stretch for a few centimeters down into the filament. A lump is a place where the size of the region surpasses its position in the rankings. Neck-downs, on the other hand, refer to locations where the size is considerably smaller than what is stated. This can lead to jamming and stripping, but this is unusual, especially if the filament is made by a reputable company. For this reason, "dirt cheap" filament is often discouraged.

In conclusion, each of the materials has its advantages and limitations, so you should carefully consider them before deciding which one to use. Consider what you need to print and how it will be used before making a decision.

Many people claim **PLA** is the best material to start with for novices, and you should give it a go to see if that's the case for you.

Summary

In order to understand how a 3D printer works, you need to know about its hardware. **Fused Deposition Modeling (FDM)** is the most common way to make 3D objects on a desktop. A few **3D printers** can make things out of metal and other materials. They can also make things out of glass, ceramic, wax, and other materials. Some printers can get very hot, and more care should be taken if there are children around. In home 3D printers, **ABS** and **PLA** are the two materials that most people use, but there are many more.

This is how it works: At the end of the tube, there are two holes that range in size from 0.02 mm to 0.08 mm. The filament is fed into the extruder, where it is heated to a temperature that will melt it.

This is how FDM printers work. Extruding the heated filament out of the nozzles, each object is covered at the same time.

This is how these 3D printers work: They use a UV light beam to harden a pool of resin. Most people use PLA and AB fibers for 3D printing.

PLA is a plastic made from plants, and AB is made from petroleum. It's up to you to choose the best material for your project. There are both good and bad things about each one. There are two types of thermal plastics: ABS and polylactic acid (PLA). People who warm them up make them smooth and flexible, and people who cool them down make them hard. Three tests must be passed by a material before it can be used in **3D printing**, including how it can be stored and how it can be worked with.

PLA can break down when it comes into contact with drinking water at very high temperatures. There are a lot of **3D printers** that don't have this problem. PLA-printed goods have a bright look and feel. It is powerful and stiffer than **ABS.** Intricate pin-joints make it a little more difficult to work with.

In order to get better results, make sure the material cools down properly. Each extruder in an inkjet printer is made to use filament of a certain thickness. Some printers are made to use special diameters, which may be a little thicker than the standard thickness. Starting out with **PLA** is the best way to learn how to make things. You should give it a try!

C h a p t e r   8

Making Money with Your 3D Printer

While **3D printing** is still a relatively new concept for many people, now is an ideal time for you to generate a speedy income in this field. Making money from 3D printing isn't as popular as it should be, but since everyone has a 3D printer at home, you have a unique opportunity to do so.

There are a slew of advantages to using 3D printing. Selling your 3D designs or teaching others how to print them can still be done even if you don't own a printer. You have to dig a little to see where the money is coming from, no matter where you are in the printing or development process.

1. Your designs should be sold.

One of the best ways to generate income with a 3D printer is by utilizing a **3D inkjet printer**. It's perfectly possible to sell your designs to someone who already has (or wants to use) an inkjet printer.

You can open a *3D inkjet printer business* on **Shapeways.** The Shapeways.com website allows you to sell your designs and models to the general public. Print-on-demand means that no product is created until a customer places an order.

Additionally, **Shapeways** provides you with all the tools you need to build a website, and it includes a tool known as the **"Custom Maker"** that lets you personalize the design of your 3D designs, making them more appealing and unique for your customers.

2. Sell Your Own 3D Prints
There are many places where you can sell your 3D-printed items, including **Facebook, eBay, Etsy,** and other online marketplaces. **Shopify** is an additional e-commerce platform that works well for small firms, although it's more expensive.

Another strategy to promote your 3D prints is to tell these potential consumers that you can print for them and everything they need to order from you and wait for the printing to be completed.

Then, if you have a 3D printer, you can print your ideas at home or have them made at a 3D printing service like **Shapeways** or another. You've made money with 3D printing if you send the print to the customer.

3. The third step is to build prototypes.

Offering 3D printing prototype assistance to local engineering firms is another way to profit from the technology. As a 3D developer, this is a great way to avoid having to deal with the printing process yourself. The only thing you need to do is hand over the design of the products and the printing to them. Printing services or on-site printing capabilities are likely already in place.

4. Students Should Be Taught About 3D Printing

3D printing has become a hot topic among many people, particularly students who are pursuing careers in 3D design or 3D printing. If you teach students how to set up and utilize their 3D printers, you can charge a fee for your services as a teacher.

Ads on social media and job listing websites are good

places to start if you're having trouble finding 3D printing teaching jobs.

5. Make a duplicate for a friend

With the growth of **3D Hubs** and **Make XYZ**, there is an almost instantaneous way to become a 3D inkjet printer owner. As a result, you'll get a lot of calls from local clients who want to see 3D printed stuff done.

Companies, consumers, and busy technicians are all looking for 3D printing assistance. You'll be the primary provider of that service, whether it's done in person or online.

A 3D model and printing sales process that is equivalent to custom options is available to jewelry designers. However, if you have an inkjet printer or whatever, you could do it on your own.

Find electroplaters in your area and see if you can pool your resources. We collaborate with anyone who has access to an inkjet printer, but you may be able to find artists in your area who are willing to take on a new project, and then offer to coat your photos in nickel, gold, or silver.

Look for a *computer graphics (CG) expert or CG animator* and work together to create real 3D drawings of animated character types-or go bigger and look for licensing options, as **White Clouds** has done.

Top Desktop & Mobile 3D Printer Apps

3D printing can be done at any time and from any location. In addition to desktop and laptop computers, there are apps for **3D printing** that don't even require you to download. With a 3D inkjet printer app, you can see files on the go, design if you want to convert 2D photos to 3D, and more. While at work, from your desk, or at home, you may find yourself needing to focus on 3D tasks. Look at these applications; they're the coolest.

The Android version of a 3D printer app

On your Android device, you can use **MakerBot's Thingiverse app** to find new ideas for 3D printing or to publish a freshly created object to the community. Adding to your collection and sending it to the MakerBot app is also possible with this application.

Using **GCode Simulator**, you can simulate printing your 3D models and examine them for errors before you actually submit them to your inkjet printer. Simulating in real-time (taking as long as your inkjet printer would take) or in a fast-forward mode is an option. When you have a print-ready document, **GCode** Info analyzes it to determine the number of levels and estimated printing time.

If you want to know how much it will cost to print and assemble your project, the **3D Printing Cost Calculator** is an excellent tool. Input materials, filament size, spool weight, spool cost, and printing volume in millimeters; it will do all the math for you. You can use this program to automate the process if your 3D inkjet printer's native app (the software/user interface that came with it) does not do it for you.

ModelAN3DPro has a variety of options for creating 3D models on your mobile device, including the ability to import stored **OBJ** data files and share screenshots. This Google Android app for a 3D inkjet printer works with 3D cell phones and allows for native 3D viewing.

iOS Apps that allow you to use 3D printing.

The **e-Drawings app** is a 3D image viewer for mobile devices with a few special capabilities. It is possible to have both an **IOS** and an **Android version**. As a result of the IOS release, you can view the 3D picture in your environment through your phone's camera, allowing you to experience augmented reality. Cross-sectioning, measurements, as well as the ability to submit your desired file through email are all included in the professional editions of the program.

An IOS app is available in order to use the **Makerbot 3D inkjet printer**. Using this app, you can monitor and control your printing from your smartphone. For those that need to approve and print while on the go, this software will save you time.

BotQueue is a mobile printing queue for small businesses with more than one **3D inkjet printer**, allowing you to queue printing jobs and control printing from wherever you are. In order to produce the vast majority of your 3D printers, it was designed to Before you can use its mobile capabilities, you'll need to install it on your computer **(Mac or Linux).**

Apps for the desktop and the web

There are a few free desktop 3D printing programs. **Meshmixer** can be used to create a new object from scratch as well as to merge two or more 3D objects.

There are many wonderful web-based programs for those who prefer a larger screen when producing. Modeling appears to be a common theme here. They all have their own features that might help you develop your 3D drawings, nevertheless.

Tinker Cad, an online service, can be used to create *3D design modeling software*. There is no need to download anything other than your own creations, which may be exported to formats such as **OBJ** or **STL** for **3D printing** or **SVG** for laser light cutting.

Tinkercad supports a wide range of 3D printers, including **MakerBot, Polar Cloud, Treatstock,** and **Voodoo**. In addition, <u>PNG exporting and transmitting the 3D design to</u> <u>Autodesk Fusion 360 and 3D regions are other functions.</u>

Parametric Parts is a *3D design* program that uses parameters to create new designs. This open-source service gives you access to third-party components from which to create your own designs.

Make 3D objects from 2D sketches by using the shape methods in **Illustrator**. You can upload your picture in the dark and then adjust the website's width in the gray. <u>In</u> <u>addition to ceramics and sandstone, they can print your</u> <u>design in metals and other 3D-printed materials.</u>

<u>If you want to encrypt your 3D creations before sending</u> <u>them,</u> **Disarming Corruptor** <u>is an interesting Macintosh</u> <u>software.</u> An encryption code and an application are required by the recipient in order to see the document in its original form.

One such web-based drawing app is **Sketch Up**. You can find 3D drawings generated by other users and import them directly into your assignment for control or usage as you see fit. Moreover, this **3D inkjet printer program** can be downloaded as well.

Summary

Making money from 3D printing isn't as popular as it should be. Selling your designs or teaching others how to print them can still be done even if you don't own a printer. Shapeways.com allows you to sell your designs and models to the general public. Offering 3D printing prototype assistance is another way to profit from the technology. If you teach students how to set up and use 3D printers, you can charge a fee for your services as a teacher.

3D printing can be done at any time and from any location. Using **GCode Simulator**, you can simulate printing 3D models and examine them for errors before you actually submit them to your inkjet printer. The e-Drawings app is a 3D image viewer for mobile devices with a few special capabilities. **ModelAN3DPro** lets you import previously saved **OBJ files** and share screenshots. **Tinkercad** supports a wide range of 3D printers, including **MakerBot, Polar Cloud, Treatstock,** and **Voodoo.** **BotQueue** is a mobile printing queue for small businesses with more than one 3D inkjet printer. There are many wonderful web-based programs for those who prefer a larger screen when producing.

Free Bonus

Grab My *"Social Media Marketing Made Simple"* Ebook For **FREE!**

Today you can grab your copy of my Free e-book titled – **Social Media Marketing made Simple**. Best of all, it won't cost you a thing.

Click the image above to **Download the Book**, and also Subscribe for Free books, giveaways, and new releases by me.

https://mayobook.com/milton

Feedback

I'd like to express my gratitude to you for choosing to read this book, Thank you. I hope you got what you wanted from it. Your feedback as to whether I succeeded or not is greatly appreciated, as I went to great lengths to make it as helpful as possible.

I would be grateful if you could write me a review on the product detail page about how this book has helped you. Your review means a lot to me, as I would love to hear about your successes. Nothing makes me happier than knowing that my work has aided someone in achieving their goals and progressing in life; which would likewise motivate me to improve and serve you better, and also encourage other readers to get influenced positively by my work. Your feedback means so much to me, and I will never take it for granted.

However, if there is something you would love to tell me as to improve on my work, it is possible that you are not impressed enough, or you have a suggestion, errors, recommendation, or criticism for us to improve on; we are profoundly sorry for your experience (remember, we are human, we are not perfect, and we are constantly striving to improve).

Rather than leaving your displeasure feedback on the retail product page of this book, please send your feedback, suggestion, or complaint to us via E-mail to **"milton@mayobook.com"** so that action can be taken quickly to ensure necessary correction, improvement, and implementation for the better reading experience.

I want you to enjoy your reading experience; your satisfaction is my **#1** priority. You are well appreciated for reading this book.

Thank you, have a wonderful day!

About The Author

I'm a programmer, designer, and entrepreneur. I'm a full-stack developer and have been doing this for over seven years. I've worked for a few different start-ups and larger companies and am looking to start a new adventure. I love to learn, especially about technology and software. I like to build things and share my knowledge with others.

I don't care if you're a big company or a small business, I'm here to help you succeed.

I also enjoy the outdoors and hiking, so I can also offer some technical advice on that front. I've worked on a few different platforms and technologies including Node.js, HTML5, CSS3, and Sass, React, Redux, and Flux, Vue.js, Java, Groovy, and Grails, Ruby on Rails, WordPress, Magento, and Joomla, Django.

I want to make sure you're getting the most out of your devices, apps, and gadgets. I've worked with both large and small businesses. As a developer, I'm not just interested in development, but also in helping people use their devices to improve their life. I'm interested in solving problems and making sure people are getting the best out of their tech.

Subscribe to my Newsletter to download my Free Book, and also be informed about my new releases, and giveaways here: https://mayobook.com/milton

Connect with me on my Facebook Page here: https://fb.me/miltondonrandall

Printed in the USA
CPSIA information can be obtained
at www.ICGtesting.com
LVHW012153230823
755981LV00006B/297